SKiPPiNG

GW00858666

written by Jade Smith
photographed by Ned Meldrum

The boys and girls like to play skipping at school.

They are going to play with this red skipping rope. Skipping is fun to play.

The red skipping rope can go up.

The red skipping rope can go down.

This girl is jumping in.
She jumps up,
and she jumps down.

The girl is jumping
on the rope.
The rope stops.

This boy is running in.
He jumps up, and he jumps down.

The boy is not jumping
on the rope.

This girl is hopping in.
She hops up, and she hops down.
The girl is not hopping
on the rope.

This boy is hopping in, too.
The boy is hopping
on the rope.
The rope stops.

The boys and girls
like to play with the skipping rope.
It is fun!